Our
Family
Christmas
Diary

Our Family Christmas Diary

The Colonial Williamsburg Foundation

Universe

Published by
Universe
381 Park Avenue South
New York, NY 10016

TM identifies trademark owned by
The Colonial Williamsburg Foundation

Printed in Hong Kong

Design by Harry Chester Associates

Distributed to the trade by
St. Martin's Press

ISBN 1-55550-712-3

hristmas in Colonial Williamsburg is the culmination of centuries of holiday traditions. Each winter the town's exhibition buildings, homes, and shops are trimmed with decorations made entirely of natural materials. Apples, lemons, holly berries, magnolia leaves, evergreen boughs, pineapples, seed pods, pinecones, cotton bolls, and oyster shells bring the beauty of nature into this festive season. Visitors and residents join together in the caroling and the outdoor games, feast at "groaning board" tables, delight in the musical recitals, and share in many other activities during this fortnight of joyous celebration.

In eighteenth-century Virginia Christmas was primarily a family time. Christmas day was observed as a holy day, with the entire family attending services at the parish church. Servants and laborers enjoyed a day of rest, and some may have received small gifts that day. "The balls, the fox-hunts, the fine entertainments, and the good fellowship" that ensued were described in diaries of the period. Santa Claus and his reindeer had not yet become a part of the folklore of Christmas.

Christmas as it is celebrated today in Virginia's restored colonial capital is a historical composite of this special holiday. Eighteenth-, nineteenth-, and early twentieth-century customs are kept alive through the years without the intrusions of modern day commercialism, bringing to those who share in the Williamsburg Christmas the priceless gift of tradition.

CHRISTMAS ____

Holiday Friends
And Revelers

Holiday Food
And Spirits

 Our Favorite Christmas Memories

Holiday Gifts And Treats

(Place Family Photo Here)

CHRISTMAS _____

Holiday Friends And Revelers

Holiday Food And Spirits

Our Favorite Christmas Memories

Holiday Gifts And Treats

(Place Family Photo Here)

CHRISTMAS ____

Holiday Friends And Revelers

Holiday Food And Spirits

Our Favorite Christmas Memories

Holiday Gifts And Treats

(Place Family Photo Here)

CHRISTMAS _____

Holiday Friends And Revelers

Holiday Food And Spirits

Our Favorite Christmas Memories

Holiday Gifts And Treats

(Place Family Photo Here)

CHRISTMAS ____

Holiday Friends And Revelers

Holiday Food And Spirits

Our Favorite Christmas Memories

Holiday Gifts And Treats

(Place Family Photo Here)

CHRISTMAS _____

Holiday Friends
And Revelers

Holiday Food
And Spirits

Our Favorite Christmas Memories

 Holiday Gifts And Treats

(Place Family Photo Here)

CHRISTMAS _____

Holiday Friends And Revelers

Holiday Food And Spirits

Our Favorite Christmas Memories

Holiday Gifts And Treats

(Place Family Photo Here)

CHRISTMAS _____

Holiday Friends And Revelers

Holiday Food And Spirits

Our Favorite Christmas Memories

Holiday Gifts And Treats

(Place Family Photo Here)

CHRISTMAS ____

Holiday Friends And Revelers

Holiday Food And Spirits

Our Favorite Christmas Memories

Holiday Gifts And Treats

(Place Family Photo Here)

CHRISTMAS ____

Holiday Friends And Revelers

Holiday Food And Spirits

Our Favorite Christmas Memories

Holiday Gifts And Treats

(Place Family Photo Here)

CHRISTMAS _____

Holiday Friends And Revelers

Holiday Food And Spirits

Our Favorite Christmas Memories

Holiday Gifts And Treats

(Place Family Photo Here)

CHRISTMAS _____

Holiday Friends And Revelers

Holiday Food And Spirits

Our Favorite Christmas Memories

Holiday Gifts And Treats

(Place Family Photo Here)

CHRISTMAS ____

Holiday Friends
And Revelers

Holiday Food
And Spirits

Our Favorite Christmas Memories

Holiday Gifts And Treats

(Place Family Photo Here)

CHRISTMAS ____

Holiday Friends And Revelers

Holiday Food And Spirits

Our Favorite Christmas Memories

Holiday Gifts And Treats

(Place Family Photo Here)

CHRISTMAS _____

Holiday Friends And Revelers

Holiday Food And Spirits

Our Favorite Christmas Memories

Holiday Gifts And Treats

(Place Family Photo Here)

CHRISTMAS ____

Holiday Friends And Revelers

Holiday Food And Spirits

Our Favorite Christmas Memories

Holiday Gifts And Treats

(Place Family Photo Here)

CHRISTMAS ____

Holiday Friends
And Revelers

Holiday Food
And Spirits

Our Favorite Christmas Memories

Holiday Gifts And Treats

(Place Family Photo Here)

CHRISTMAS ____

Holiday Friends And Revelers

Holiday Food And Spirits

Our Favorite Christmas Memories

Holiday Gifts And Treats

(Place Family Photo Here)

CHRISTMAS ____

Holiday Friends And Revelers

Holiday Food And Spirits

Our Favorite Christmas Memories

Holiday Gifts And Treats

(Place Family Photo Here)

CHRISTMAS ___

Holiday Friends And Revelers

Holiday Food And Spirits

Our Favorite Christmas Memories

Holiday Gifts And Treats

(Place Family Photo Here)

Our Favorite Christmas Recipes

Our Favorite Christmas Recipes

Our Favorite Christmas Recipes

Our Favorite Christmas Recipes

Christmas Card List

Christmas Card List

Christmas Card List

More Favorite Photos and Holiday Cards

More Favorite Photos and Holiday Cards

More Favorite Photos and Holiday Cards

More Favorite Photos and Holiday Cards